THE
Teddy Bear
BIRTHDAY
BOOK

Design
Jill Coote

Editorial
Nicola Dent

Photography
Teddy bears: Neil Sutherland
Cookery: Peter Barry

Photographic Assistance
Nigel Duffield
Jo Finnis
Adele Hayward
Sally Strugnell

Typesetting
Julie Smith

Production
Ruth Arthur
Sally Connolly
Neil Randles

Director of Production
Gerald Hughes

CLB 3324
© 1993 Colour Library Books Ltd.,
Godalming, Surrey, England.
All rights reserved.
Colour separation by Advance
Laser Graphic Arts, Singapore.
Printed and bound by New
Interlitho, Italy.
ISBN 1 85833 076 9

THE
Teddy Bear
BIRTHDAY
BOOK

Colour Library Books

January

New Year's bears on New Year's Day,
Time for jokes and games and play,
Lots of fun and loads of laughs,
We don't live our lives by halves.
Sledging into this New Year,
We're full of hope, full of cheer,
Good or bad the year may send,
We'll see it through, right to the end!

# January

CAPRICORN
22 December - 20 January

AQUARIUS
21 January - 18 February

1

New Year's Day

2

3

4

'T stands for Teddy,
He's really a dear,
And not at all fierce,
Although he's a bear.'

Anon

5

6

Epiphany
Twelfth Night

7

8

1935: birth of Elvis Presley, famous U.S. singer, who was inundated with teddies after the release of his song 'Teddy Bear', from the 1957 film *Loving You*.

9

10

11

In the 1950s, the Boulgom Co. began stuffing its bears with foam rubber, replacing the more rigid excelsior stuffing and causing a breakthrough in hugability!

12

13

14

15

16

17

18

1882: birth of A.A. Milne, who wrote the world's best-selling teddy bear book, featuring cuddly Winnie-the-Pooh.

19

1971: Senior Under Officer Edward Bear – a mascot of Great Britain's RMAS Parachute Club since the early 1950s – made his record-breaking 400th jump!

20

21

Most historians agree that Theodore Roosevelt, the 26th American president, lent his name to the teddy bear, but that doesn't keep them from arguing about it. Some say that the name comes from his contemporary, King Edward VII of England, also known as Ted, whose enthusiasm for animals in general and bears in particular matched that of the irrepressible T.R.

 *January*

22

23

'Bear, bear, don't go away,
To come back some other day.
I will love you if you stay,
I will love you any way.'
Early 20th-century greeting card

24

1948: Biffo the Bear, a cartoon
character created by Dudley D.
Watkins, was first introduced on
the front cover of *The Beano*, a
popular English children's comic.

25

26

27

28

Fur, once made from real animal hair,
then from mohair plush – the silky
wool of the Angora goat – now tends
to be made of a wool and cotton blend,
velveteen, suede or a man-made fabric.

Honey and Apple Tart

*'Isn't it funny How a bear likes honey
Buzz! Buzz! Buzz! I wonder why he does?'* Winnie-the-Pooh

Serves 6

Pastry:
90g/3oz wholemeal flour
90g/3oz plain white flour
90g/3oz unsalted butter
1 egg yolk
3 tbsps cold water

Filling:
1 tbsp honey
280ml/½ pint apple purée
2 egg yolks
2 tbsps ground almonds
3 large eating apples, thinly
   sliced
A little pale soft brown sugar
3 tbsps clear honey, warmed to
   glaze

Preheat oven: 190°C/375°F/Gas
Mark 5. **Pastry**: mix together the
flours and rub in the butter. Beat
1 egg yolk with 2 tbsps of water
and blend to form a soft dough,
adding extra water if necessary.
Roll out to line a 23cm/9-inch flan
ring; pinch up the edges well and
prick the base. **Filling**: mix the
apple purée with the honey, egg
yolks and ground almonds and
spread evenly over the base of
the pastry case. Arrange the apple
slices in overlapping, concentric
circles on top of the filling. Dust
with soft brown sugar. Bake for
35-40 minutes, or until golden.
Glaze with the warmed honey.

February

And these two bears, so large and small,
Are just the greatest friends of all.
Is one too short and one too big?
They really couldn't care a fig!
February chums sit side by side,
One to another they quietly confide.

February

1

2

Groundhog Day in America,
when the groundhog emerges
from hibernation. If he sees his
shadow it is said that there will
be six more weeks of winter.
An older tradition in Europe
says that the bear wakes up
from his winter sleep on Shrove
Tuesday and if he returns to
his lair there will be 40 more
days of winter, but if he stays
awake, spring is approaching!

3

4

5

1968: an original illustration
of Winnie-the-Pooh, drawn
by E.H. Shepard, was sold for
an exceptional £1,200 when
auctioned at Sotheby's, London.

6

7

Sir Archibald Ormsby-Gore,
'Whose ample forehead
I could wet with tears,
Whose half-moon ears
received my confidence,
Who made me laugh,
who never let me down'
was the much-loved ted of
Sir John Betjeman, the
poet whose words perfectly
capture the loyal friend-
ship of a teddy bear.

February

8

9

10

'Libearty', a campaign for the prevention of cruelty to bears, was launched in February 1992 by the World Society for the Protection of Animals.

11

12

13

14

Saint Valentine's Day
Several U.S. 'artist bears' have been based on legendary lovers, including Romeo and Juliet, Robin Hood and Maid Marion, and the fairy tale Beauty and the Beast!

February

15

16

In February 1914 J.S. Baker's the
Bruin Boys – perhaps the earliest
cartoon teddies to exist – appeared
on the front page of *The Rainbow*,
celebrating the launch of this comic.

17

18

1990: as a gesture of peace,
teddy bears were exchanged
over Germany's former
East/West border at Check-
point Charlie, in Berlin.

19

20

21

Many countries are very nationalistic and proud about their bears. Among the famous names are: Britain's Rupert, Winnie-the-Pooh and Paddington — suitably attired against the country's rainy weather; France has Gros Nounours and Prosper, with his stylish black velvet jacket; America has Smokey and Fozzie bears; Germany has Bussi Bear; Spain Bimbo; Russia Mishka, and Australia has Billy Bluegum, a koala.

February

22

1965: Italian Alpine climber Walter Bonatti climbed the treacherous North Face of the Matterhorn, with the support of his tiny companion Zissi the Bear.

23

24

25

26

27

28 / 29

Today teddy bears are often used by the police, counsellors, medical staff and other professionals to help communicate with young victims of accident, trauma and abuse.

Seville Marmalade

'Mrs. Bird was always going on about Paddington's fondness for marmalade, but it was noticeable she was never without a spare jar in the larder in case of emergency.' A Bear Called Paddington

Makes approximately 7 jars

Ingredients:
6 Seville (bitter) oranges
2 lemons
2kg/4lb sugar
2¾ litres/4½ pints water

Wash the oranges and lemons. Quarter the fruit and slice thinly, catching all the juice. Tie the pips in muslin. Place the fruit and pips in a large bowl with the water, cover and leave for 24 hours. Next, simmer the mixture gently until the liquid has thickened and reduced to about half and the peel has softened – usually between 2-2¹/₂ hours.

Discard the pips and add the warmed sugar. Boil rapidly for 10-15 minutes and then test for setting. Skim immediately. Cool for about 15 minutes, stir gently and pour into warmed jars. Cover and seal.

Combinations of other citrus fruits – lime, lemon, grapefruit, sweet oranges and satsumas – make interesting variations.

March

March, march, marching bears,
Marching up and down,
Forget about those mad March hares,
The bears are back in town.
March, march, marching bears,
Marching round and round,
March winds blow away your cares,
And teds won't let you down.

March

ARIES
20 March - 20 April

Saint David's Day

1

2

3

4

5

Sleepy Bear, designed to soothe babies with its maternal, pulse-like sound, was produced in Australia in March 1980, based on the successful U.S. Rock-a-bye Bear.

6

7

*The first ever teddy bears to be made
date from 1903. One is Friend Petz,
once owned by Margarete Steiff who
founded the world-famous German toy
and bear company, Steiff & Co. The
other is Teddy's Bear, which was sent to
President Roosevelt by its creator,
Morris Michtom, who went on to found
the Ideal Novelty and Toy Company.
These bears are on display in the
Giengen Steiff offices, Germany, and the
Smithsonian Institute, U.S., respectively.*

March

8

9

10

1978: Super Ted, created by Mike Young, first appeared in print. This bear, with his special powers, went on to feature in a televised cartoon series in the 1980s.

11

12

1903: an order for 3,000 teds – the first interest shown in this new toy – was placed by a large New York store at Germany's Leipzig Fair.

13

14

March

15

16

17

Saint Patrick's Day

18

19

Saint Joseph's Day

20

21

1912: birth of British actor Peter Bull, author of *Bear With Me* and *The Teddy Bear Book* which, published in 1969, helped spark off a revival in the teddy world.

*Although the ancient Greeks produced many wonderful things, the idea of having a stuffed bear for a companion never occurred to them. But they did give us a pair of words to help describe our feelings about teddy bears: arktos, or bear, and philos, or beloved. Put them together and the word is **arctophile**. You and me!*

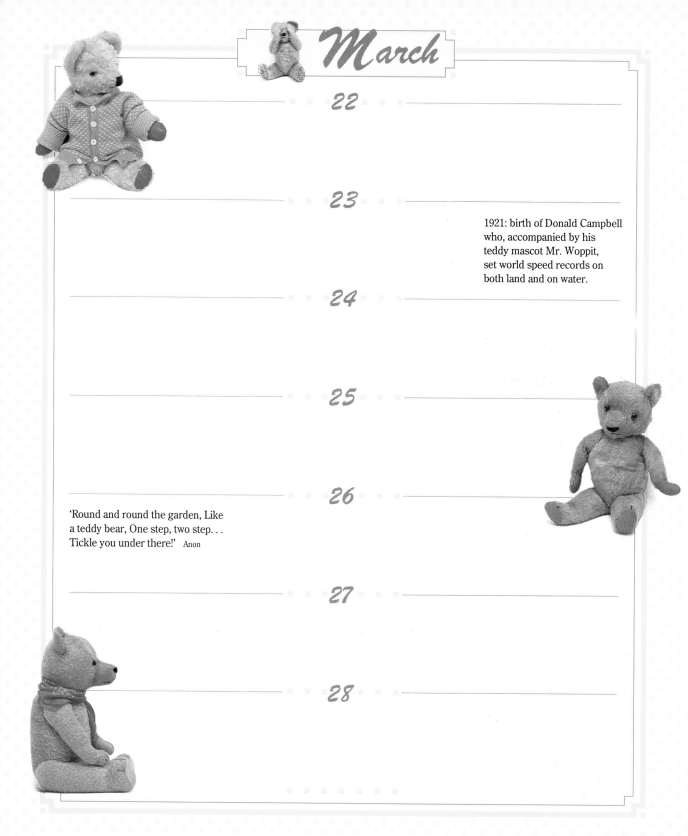

March

22

23

1921: birth of Donald Campbell who, accompanied by his teddy mascot Mr. Woppit, set world speed records on both land and on water.

24

25

26

'Round and round the garden, Like a teddy bear, One step, two step. . . Tickle you under there!' Anon

27

28

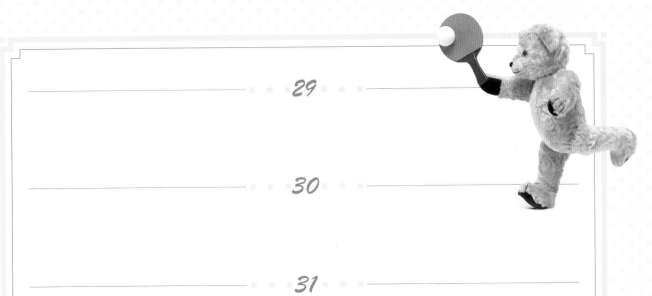

29

30

31

1950: birthday of America's
Smokey Bear, the loveable
mascot used in the U.S.
Forest Service campaign for
the prevention of forest fire.

Honey and Ricotta Pancakes

Even the Encyclopaedia Britannica *states that most bears enjoy
honey, a fact well supported by many well-known teds!*

Serves 4

Batter:
120g/4oz plain flour
1 egg, beaten
280ml/½ pint milk
1 tbsp vegetable oil
Juice and pared rind of 1 lemon
Filling:
Grated rind of ½ lemon
225g/8oz curd or Ricotta cheese
2 tbsps raisins
1 tbsp pine nuts, chopped
Sauce:
60ml/4 tbsps clear honey
Juice of ½ lemon
1 tbsp raisins
1 tbsp pine nuts

Batter: mix the flour and a pinch
of salt making a well in the centre.
Whisk the egg and milk and stir
into the flour, beating to a
smooth batter. Heat a little oil in
a pan, add some batter spreading
as thinly as possible. Cook until
brown on the base and turn over
to cook the reverse. **Filling**: beat
the cheese and lemon rind until
soft; mix in the raisins and pine
nuts. Divide the filling among the
hot pancakes, either rolling them
up or folding them into triangles.
Sauce: mix the ingredients in a
small pan and warm gently. Pour
over the pancakes and decorate
with twists of lemons.

April

Two teds wake up at the start of Spring,
Birds sing loudly, scent of flowers drifts in.
They look to the future, and back to the past,
As they consider their lengthy, Winter fast.
And one turns to the other and loudly proclaims:
'I've had quite enough of this long sleeping game!'

April

TAURUS
21 April - 21 May

— 1 —

1972: a spoof report appeared in the *Veterinary Record* entitled 'Some Observations on the Diseases of *Brunus edwardii (Species nova)'*!

All Fools' Day

— 2 —

1869: birth of Clifford K. Berryman, U.S. political cartoonist particularly renowned for his 'Drawing the Line in Mississippi' cartoon, which inspired the name 'Teddy's Bear'.

— 3 —

— 4 —

— 5 —

— 6 —

— 7 —

'My very littlest, smallest ted, Is much too wee to come to bed. He sleeps inside a walnut shell, Which fits around him very well.' Paul Richardson

 *April*

8

9

10

It is reputed that a large Hamley's teddy bear was used to test the first parachute prototype!

11

12

13

14

The Steiff Club was officially established in April 1992 to supply regular information, club magazines and a limited edition teddy to its thousands of members every year.

April

15

1912: Gatti, a 1907 Gerbruder Bing bear belonging to the ship's catering manager, survived the tragic sinking of the mighty liner *Titanic*.

16

17

18

19

20

The tremendously popular U.S. magazine, *Teddy Bear and Friends*, was first published in Spring 1983.

Rolf Gerhard **21**

22

23

1928: birth of Shirley Temple
who, in the 1930s, owned one
of the largest *hugs* of bears as
thousands sent her teddies, some
bigger than the tiny star herself.

Saint George's Day

24

25

Saint Mark's Day

26

27

28

Honeyed Apple Mousse

'. . .his nose told him it was indeed honey, and his tongue came out and began to polish up his mouth, ready for it.' Winnie-the-Pooh

Serves 6

3 lbs dessert apples
3 tbsps butter
Grated rind of 1 lemon
45g/1½oz honey
15g/½ oz unflavoured gelatine
60ml/2 fl oz water
250ml/9 fl oz double cream
120g/4oz sugar
430ml/¾ pint water
10 shelled walnuts, to decorate

Peel, core and grate all but two apples. Put 1 tbsp of butter into a pan with the grated apple and cook gently until the juice starts to run; increase the heat and cook to a pulp. Add the lemon rind and cook until a purée. Remove from the heat and add the honey. Dissolve the gelatine in 60ml/2 fl oz water and when clear add to the apple purée. Cool. Whip the cream and fold gently into the mixture; turn into an oiled mould and leave to set. Peel, quarter and core the rest of the apples. Dissolve the sugar in 430ml/¾ pint water; boil for a few minutes and add the apple. Reduce the heat and poach for 7 minutes. Drain. Add the rest of the butter to the syrup and boil until reduced to a caramel. Remove from heat and coat the walnuts with mixture. Cool. Turn out the mousse and decorate with poached apples and nuts.

May

Counting the daisies
Now that it's May,
The breeze ruffles our fur
In a ticklish way.
Sitting on the grass,
Listening to the bees,
Playing hide and seek
Down among the trees.

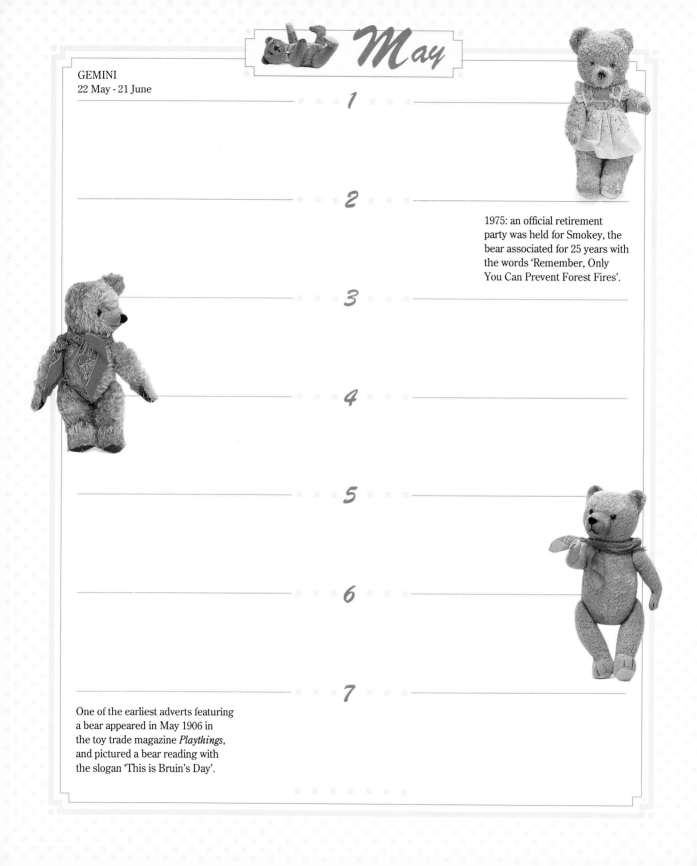

May

GEMINI
22 May - 21 June

1

2

1975: an official retirement
party was held for Smokey, the
bear associated for 25 years with
the words 'Remember, Only
You Can Prevent Forest Fires'.

3

4

5

6

7

One of the earliest adverts featuring
a bear appeared in May 1906 in
the toy trade magazine *Playthings*,
and pictured a bear reading with
the slogan 'This is Bruin's Day'.

In 1903, at about the same time the Wright Brothers were trying to figure out how to fly, Richard Steiff was sketching bears at the Stuttgart Zoo. His Aunt Margarete transformed his drawings into a Mohair bear. . .

. . .the family exhibited this bear at the Leipzig Toy Fair. No one seemed interested until the fair's last day, when an American placed an order for 3,000! The rest, as they say, is history.

May

8

World Red Cross Day

9

10

Red plush Alfonzo, a teddy gift from the Grand Duke of Russia to his daughter Princess Xenia, was sold in 1989 at London's Christie's for an incredible £12,100 ($19,800).

11

12

13

1905: to help prevent fraud, the *Knopf im Ohr*, or Button in Ear, was patented as the official trademark of the German Steiff teddy and toy company.

14

May

15

16

17

18

1919: birth of world-renowned
Dame Margot Fonteyn,
outstanding British ballerina
and, with her husband, a
proud teddy bear owner!

19

20

1990: official publication day of
Hugglets Teddy Bear Magazine, a
popular English teddy publication
with some 10,000 readers in the
United Kingdom alone.

21

It is believed that the first teddy was made by Morris Michtom of New York, who sent his prototype to President Theodore Roosevelt asking if he could name it after him. The handwritten reply said, '. . . I don't believe my name will do much for the image of your stuffed bear, but you have my permission to use it'. The talented T.R. was obviously not blessed with the gift of prophecy!

May

22

23

'Teddy Bear cannot be seen
Until his face is nice and clean.
My teddy nearly always cries
Because the soap goes in his eyes.'

Rhyme from early postcard

24

25

26

27

1979: the first British 'Great
Teddy Bear Rally and Honey
Fair' was held at Longleat,
stately home of the Marquis
of Bath and his teddy Clarence.

28

Wendy Boston Playsafe Toys must have produced a ripple in the bear world in 1954 when they produced the first nylon, machine-washable teddy bear!

Blueberry Oat Bars

Bears are almost always depicted as being very food orientated, with berries and honey being all-time favourites!

Crust:
150g/5oz rolled oats
175g/6oz plain flour
175g/6oz soft brown sugar
60g/2oz chopped nuts
½ tsp bicarbonate of soda
175g/6oz butter, melted

Filling:
120g/4oz sugar
225g/8oz blueberries, fresh or frozen
3 tbsps water
2 tbsps cornflour
1 tbsp lemon juice

Preheat oven: 180°C/350°F/Gas Mark 4. **Crust**: combine the dry ingredients and add the butter,

mixing until crumbly. Reserve 1 cup of the mixture and press the remainder into a greased 28x18cm/11x7-inch baking dish. Cook for 10 minutes. **Filling**: combine the blueberries, sugar and 2 tbsps of water in pan. Bring to the boil and simmer uncovered for 2 minutes. Combine cornflour, 1 tbsp water and lemon juice; mix well. Slowly stir into the blueberry mixture, cooking for about 30 seconds, or until thickened. Spread filling over partly baked base and sprinkle with the rest of the oat mixture. Cook for 20 minutes. Cool and cut into about 15 bars. Store tightly covered.

June

Off in our sports car,
Down to the sea,
Bears in the fast lane,
We're fancy free.
We are the smartest –
Our car is bright red,
But if we get back late,
Please help us to bed!

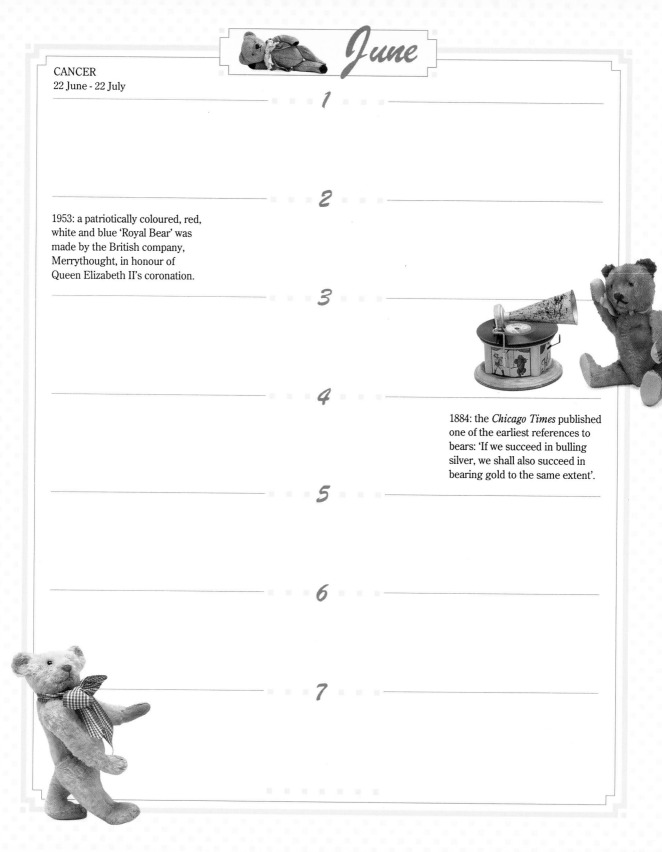

June

CANCER
22 June - 22 July

1

2

1953: a patriotically coloured, red, white and blue 'Royal Bear' was made by the British company, Merrythought, in honour of Queen Elizabeth II's coronation.

3

4

1884: the *Chicago Times* published one of the earliest references to bears: 'If we succeed in bulling silver, we shall also succeed in bearing gold to the same extent'.

5

6

7

Often considered a member of the bear family, technically the koala is a marsupial and the panda a relative of the raccoon. In the teddy world, however, both are usually treated as honorary bears and are just as loveable!

June

8

9

The Vietnamese boat people were welcomed with teddies when they arrived in Britain in June 1979.

10

11

1979: 'Arctophilia Runs Amok' was the headline in America's *Time* magazine, following the spectacular teddy convention held at Longleat in Britain the previous month!

12

13

14

June

15

World Children's Day

16

17

A British Collectors' Club was set up in June 1987 for those who are keen collectors of the tiny ceramic teddy figures modelled by Peter Fagan of Colour Box Miniatures.

18

19

20

21

'Fuzzy Wuzzy was a bear,
A bear was Fuzzy Wuzzy.
When Fuzzy Wuzzy lost his hair
He wasn't fuzzy wuz he?'

Traditional

Perhaps the most popular teddy song of all time is The Teddy Bear's Picnic. *The lyrics were written in 1930 by British songwriter Jimmy Kennedy to go with the music by American John Bratton. It was hoped that the song would become the official campaign song for Theodore Roosevelt in the 1908 election but, disappointingly for the composer, T.R. stepped aside from the running.*

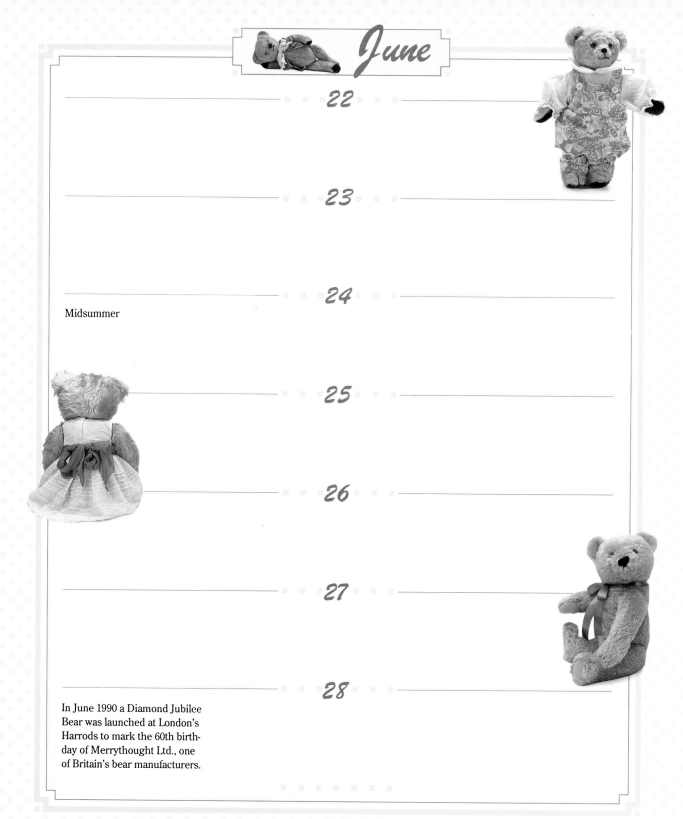

June

22

23

24

Midsummer

25

26

27

28

In June 1990 a Diamond Jubilee
Bear was launched at London's
Harrods to mark the 60th birthday of Merrythought Ltd., one
of Britain's bear manufacturers.

Saint Peter's Day

Bee Sting Cake

'Pooh didn't mind for himself, but when he thought of all the honey the bees wouldn't be making, a cold and misty day always made him feel sorry for them.' The House at Pooh Corner

Cake:
175g/6oz self-raising flour
150g/5oz butter or margarine
90g/3oz sugar
2 eggs
½ tsp vanilla essence
1-2 tbsps milk

Topping:
60g/2oz sugar
60g/4 tbsps butter
1 tbsp milk
60g/2oz flaked almonds

Filling:
60g/2oz sugar
2 tbsps cornflour
3 egg yolks
140ml/¼ pint milk
90ml/3 fl oz double cream, whipped
¼ tsp vanilla/almond essence

Preheat oven: 190°C/375°F/Gas Mark 5. **Cake**: sift flour, cream butter, and add sugar, beating until fluffy. Add vanilla and eggs, one at a time, then the milk and flour, alternating between the two until the mixture forms a thick dropping consistency. Spoon into a greased cake tin. **Topping**: mix ingredients and heat to dissolve sugar. Pour onto the cake. Bake for 25 minutes until top caramelises. **Filling**: whisk the sugar, cornflour and egg yolks until light. Pour on the milk and gently warm until the mixture coats the back of a spoon. Add essence. Cool; fold in whipped cream. Cut the cake in half, fill, and sandwich layers together.

July

Would you marry me
On this bright sunny day?
Would you marry me
Blow the dark clouds away?
Would you marry me,
The two of us together?
Please, let's marry soon
So I can hold you forever.

LEO
23 July - 23 August

1903: birth of Amy Johnson,
pioneer female aviator who,
with her teddy bear mascot,
became the first woman to fly
solo from Britain to Australia.

1

2

3

Saint Thomas' Day

4

1988: the Teddy Bear Museum
at Stratford-Upon-Avon, England,
was opened. This is now an
award-winning museum housing
hundreds of famous bears.

5

6

7

The earliest teddy bears didn't look like their descendants. They tended to be taller and leaner and their shoe-button eyes often gave them an unfriendly, vacant stare. Their arms, though, instantly suggested hugging because they were long, far out of proportion to the rest of the body. In the manner of real bears their muzzles protruded more than in modern teddies and they had a hump in the centre of their back. The paws, arms and head were all moveable and many early teds found themselves in the undignified position of resting snout on hump!

8

9

10

Officer Cadet Edward Bear,
the new mascot for Britain's
RMAS Parachute Club, made his
daring parachuting debut from
2,000 feet (610m) in July 1992.

11

12

If displaying your bear keep him
or her out of direct sunlight and
drafts, away from water pipes and
air conditioners, and out of dusty,
smoky or damp atmospheres.

13

14

July

15

Saint Swithin's Day

16

17

18

Teds play a valuable role in promoting
hospitals and charities; Pudsey Bear
is the mascot for BBC's 'Children In
Need' and Jamie for 'Help the Sick
Kids', two successful British appeals.

19

20

21

A couple of lions make a pride and a bunch of gnats a horde. A flight of larks is an exultation, a collection of cats a clutter, a barrel of monkeys a troop, and when toads gather together, it is called a knot. We have broods of chicks and gaggles of geese. But get several teds, said the late British actor Peter Bull, and you have a **hug** of bears!

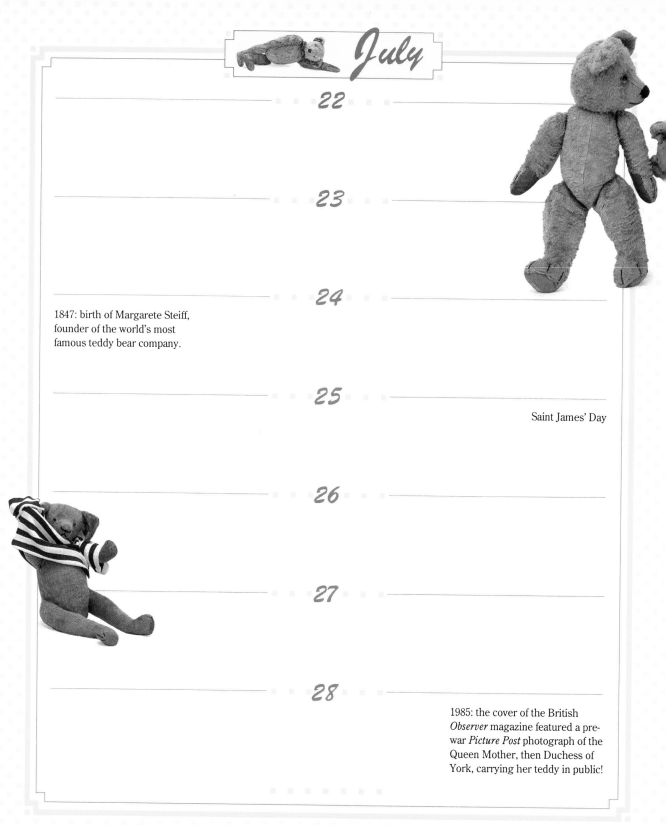

July

22

23

24

1847: birth of Margarete Steiff,
founder of the world's most
famous teddy bear company.

25

Saint James' Day

26

27

28

1985: the cover of the British
Observer magazine featured a pre-
war *Picture Post* photograph of the
Queen Mother, then Duchess of
York, carrying her teddy in public!

29

30

31

Honey and Spice Oranges

*'Honey can be runny, or really very thick, But full of
taste and oh so sweet, It's every bear's best treat!'*

Serves 4

280ml/½ pint honey
430ml/¾ pint water
2 large sprigs of fresh mint
12 whole cloves
4 large oranges
4 small sprigs of mint, to garnish

Put the honey and the water into
a pan, add the mint and cloves
and slowly bring to the boil.
Stir the mixture to dissolve the
honey and boil rapidly for 5
minutes, or until the liquid is
very syrupy. Cool completely,
then strain the mixture to
remove the mint and cloves.

Using a potato peeler, carefully
pare the rind very thinly from
one orange. Cut the pared
orange into very fine shreds,
place in a small bowl and cover
with boiling water. Allow to
stand until cold, then drain
completely, reserving only the
strips of peel. Stir the peel into
the honey syrup and chill well.
Peel the oranges completely,
removing all the skin and white
pith. Slice the oranges into thin
rounds and arrange in a pattern
on 4 individual plates. Pour the
chilled syrup over the oranges
and garnish with the sprigs of
mint just before serving.

August

The sun shines hot,
down by the sea,
As five little bears
Tuck into their tea.
Just teds having fun,
In a playful, happy mood,
In the sea and the sun
With games and with food!

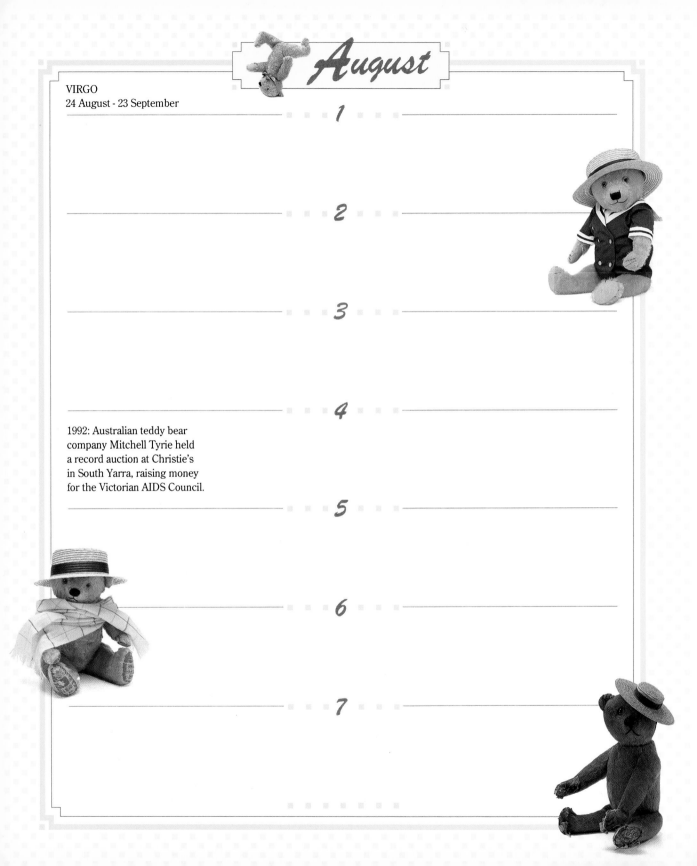

August

VIRGO
24 August - 23 September

1

2

3

4

1992: Australian teddy bear
company Mitchell Tyrie held
a record auction at Christie's
in South Yarra, raising money
for the Victorian AIDS Council.

5

6

7

The teddy bear, now a valuable collector's item, has evolved to a work of art. Today, the range of **artist bears** is rapidly widening as individual designers, now established as artists, create their own 'perfect bear', some based on certain themes, others on specific events or people. The result is that each limited edition bear is very special, very personal and, above all, totally unique.

August

8

9

10

11

1904: Billy Bluegum, a town-raised koala bear drawn by Norman Lindsay, first appeared in the weekly Australian *Sydney Bulletin*.

12

13

14

In August 1982 British manufacturer, Marconi Space and Defense Systems, designed a teddy whose eyes light up in recognition of a voice, for use as a teaching aid for deaf children.

August

15

The position of a bear's eyes is crucial to his/her personality – high and closely set is typical of an old bear, whereas low and wide set signifies a young bear.

16

17

18

19

20

Teds have often made an appearance on sets of stamps and a teddy post-mark was once produced by the Giengen post office, Germany, for the Jubilee of the Steiff factory.

21

Teds almost always stand upright, even though their natural counterparts spend most of their lives on all fours. Psychologists say the difference emphasizes the bear's human characteristics, of which it has more than any other animal, the ape included.

August

22

23

1979: New Zealand's 'First Teddy Bear Convention' was held in Auckland.

24

Saint Bartholomew's Day

25

26

27

1979: Australia's 'First Teddy Bear Convention' was held in Sydney, following an earlier, but similar, rally held four days previously in New Zealand.

28

1906: birth of Sir John Betjeman, British Poet Laureate known for his nostalgic verse, which includes one written about his beloved bear Sir Archibald Ormsby-Gore.

Honey Ice Cream with Pine Nuts

*'And the only reason for making honey is
so as I can eat it.'* Winnie-the-Pooh

Serves 4

2 tbsps honey (different kinds of
    honey vary the flavour)
500ml/18 fl oz milk
6 egg yolks
2 tbsps pine nuts (or other types
    of nuts to add variety)

Whisk the honey and the egg
yolks together for 1 minute.
Bring the milk to the boil and
pour over the egg mixture,
whisking continuously. (Ensure
you whisk briskly as you pour
the milk onto the egg mixture, as
the eggs can coagulate quickly
with the absence of sugar in this

recipe.) Pour the mixture back
into the saucepan and add the
pine nuts. Place over a very low
heat, stirring continuously, until
the sauce thickens and will coat
the back of a spoon. Allow to cool
and then pour into the bowl of an
ice cream maker. Set the machine
in motion.* Once the ice cream
has 'taken', spoon into a suitable
container and store in a freezer
until required.

* If an ice cream maker is not
available, part freeze the mixture,
whisk until smooth, then
refreeze. Whisk again and
freeze until firm.

September

September is on us, of that there's no doubt,
The hats and the scarves, they start to come out.
Season of changes, goodbye the teds wave
As the year draws on, with the passing of days.

September

LIBRA
24 September - 23 October

1

1906: first book publication of *Teddy B and Teddy G, The Roosevelt Bears; Their Adventures and Travels* written by Seymour Eaton and illustrated by V. Floyd Campbell.

2

3

4

1992: anniversary flight of Sopwith Bear – mascot of a British RAF squadron – to mark their 75th birthday and to end Sopwith's grounding since the death of his pilot owner.

5

6

7

September

8

9

Despite strictness about cleanliness
it is best not to overwash a young
child's teddy as he acquires the scent
of the baby and his/her mother, so
increasing ted's capacity to comfort.

10

11

12

Delicatessen, an Edwardian bear
belonging to British actor Peter
Bull, starred in 1980 as Aloysius in
the television adaptation of Evelyn
Waugh's *Brideshead Revisited*.

13

14

September

15

16

17

18

19

1989: Happy, a 1930s Steiff bear, was auctioned at London's Sotheby's for the record sum of £55,000 ($86,350), the highest figure ever paid for a teddy bear.

20

21

1987: the first exhibit by 'teddy bear artists' was held at the Incorporated Gallery on Madison Avenue in New York City, America.

Saint Matthew's Day

September

22

23

24

25

26

27

28

The Doll's Club of Great Britain runs a 'Home of Rest for Aged and Retired Teddies' for bears that have had an exciting adventure or been of great service during their life!

Baklava

'Honey in the morning, honey at noon, honey every
meal time, a bear's life would be sublime!'

Serves 6-8

Syrup:
340g/12oz granulated sugar
90ml/6 tbsps liquid honey
430ml/¾ pint water
1 tbsp lemon juice
Pastry:
450g/1lb package fyllo pastry
120g/4oz unsalted butter, melted
120g/4oz walnuts, almonds or
  pistachio nuts, chopped
½ tsp ground cinnamon
½ tbsp sugar

Preheat oven: 180° C/350° F/Gas
Mark 4. **Syrup**: combine all the
ingredients in a small pan,
dissolving the sugar and boiling
for 2 minutes until thick. Chill.
Pastry: place 8 pastry sheets on
a greased 30x45cm/12x18-inch
baking dish and brush with
melted butter. Mix the nuts,
sugar and spices, and spread

half the mixture over the pastry.
Cover with two more layers of
buttered pastry and the rest of
the nuts, then the remainder of
the individually buttered pastry
layers. Sprinkle with water to

keep moist. Bake for 30 minutes,
then at 220° C/425° F/Gas Mark
7 for 10 minutes, or until crisp
and brown. Pour the syrup over
the hot pastry. Cool, and cut into
diamond shapes to serve.

October

· · ·

Two teds together in the cool morning air,
Life full of fun, and life free of care.
What a joy for a bear, the wind's in our face
We're over the points and away we do race.
The steam's at full head as we speed down the track
We're so loving the ride we won't want to come back!

· · ·

SCORPIO
24 October - 22 November

— ● ● ■ *1* ■ ● ● —

A teddy starred – with famous
American actress Lillian Gish –
in the October 1950 Broadway
production of John Patrick's
The Curious Savage.

— ● ● ■ *2* ■ ● ● —

— ● ● ■ *3* ■ ● ● —

— ● ● ■ *4* ■ ● ● —

— ● ● ■ *5* ■ ● ● —

1964: Walt Disney Productions
designed Choco – a tiny bear with
a hurt arm – as a mascot and logo
for the Children's Hospital of
Orange County in Disneyland.

— ● ● ■ *6* ■ ● ● —

— ● ● ■ *7* ■ ● ● —

*Teddy bears make faithful travel companions
and have often been known to accompany
their owners in battle, travelling by plane
or ship, on tanks and guns, or in
haversacks and uniform pockets.
It is even reputed that bears have
saved lives by intercepting bullets!*

8

9

1984: Gina Campbell broke the women's world speed record on water, accompanied by Mr. Woppit, her record-holding father's bear, and Mrs. Woppit, her own teddy.

10

1958: Michael Bond's Paddington Bear – inspired by a lonely teddy the author found on the London railway station of the same name – made his first appearance in print.

11

12

13

14

1926: the first Winnie-the-Pooh book was published. This character was based on a real 1921 Farnell bear bought for the author A.A. Milne's son.

October

15

16

17

18

Saint Luke's Day

19

20

1987: the first *UK Teddy Bear Guide*, a useful directory of teddy bear businesses, shops, museums, artists, restorers and other addresses, was produced.

21

Bully Bear, a teddy designed by British actor Peter Bull for the House of Nisbet manufacturers, was launched at Britain's House of Commons in October 1980.

Teddy bears are frequently used as mascots for various sporting teams, as well as for the individual, and have been the faithful companion of many an athletic or adventuresome celebrity! In the 1980 Summer Olympic Games held at Moscow, Russia, the mascot was a bear called Mishka. And in 1956, Australia's appealing koala was considered the unofficial mascot of the Olympic Games held at Melbourne.

October

22

23

24

United Nations' Day

25

26

27

1858: birth of Theodore (Teddy) Roosevelt, the man who inspired the name 'Teddy's Bear'. This date is now celebrated as the fund-raising 'Good Bear Day'.

28

1903: birth of British author, Evelyn Waugh, who wrote *Brideshead Revisited*, which features a teddy bear called Aloysius, owned by one of the book's main characters.

29

30

31

Halloween

Honey Vermicelli

'It's very, very funny, 'Cos I know I had some honey;
'Cos it has a label on Saying HUNNY.' Winnie-the-Pooh

Serves 4

Pasta:
225g/½lb vermicelli
60g/2oz butter
45ml/3 tbsps clear honey
2 tsps sesame seeds
¼ tsp ground cinnamon
Sauce:
125ml/4 fl oz double cream
125ml/4 fl oz soured cream

Pasta: cook the vermicelli in boiling, salted water for 5 minutes, or until softened. Stir regularly with a fork to separate the noodles. Drain, and spread

the noodles out to dry on a wire tray covered with absorbent paper, or a tea towel. Leave for about an hour. Melt the butter in a small saucepan over a low heat. Add the sesame seeds and gently fry until lightly golden in colour. Stir in the honey, cinnamon and the cooked vermicelli and heat through.
Sauce: mix the double cream and soured cream together and chill. Serve the vermicelli hot, topped with the cream sauce.

Tip: use your own favourite kind of honey in this recipe.

November

Back to back, they gaze into space,
Sitting indoors in a warm, cozy place.
Toasting a crumpet, reading a book,
In chill November, 'We're snug in our nook!'

November

SAGITTARIUS
23 November - 21 December

All Saints' Day

Yesterday's growler has advanced
into the technobear of today, whose
abilities include whistling, somer-
saulting, bouncing, laughing and
possessing a 400-word vocabulary!

Guy Fawkes Day

1

2

3

4

5

6

7

Good Bears of the World is an international fund-raising organization established to provide teddy bears for hurt, hospitalized and abused children, and for the old and frail. It was the 1973 brainchild of American journalist James T. Ownby and now has over 10,000 worldwide members who buy and distribute bears to worthy causes. A fund-raising Good Bear Day is held annually on the birthday of the late Teddy Roosevelt.

November

8

1920: Rupert Bear, illustrated by Mary Tourtel, was first published as *The Adventures of a Little Lost Bear* in the British national newspaper the *Daily Express*.

9

10

1918: it is said that teddy Wilhelm, a c. 1910 Steiff, accompanied his owner Max – a servant of Emperor Wilhelm II – and the Emperor to the Dutch border to escape revolution.

Saint Martin's Day

11

12

13

14

November

15

16

1902: *The Washington Post* published a Berryman cartoon portraying President Roosevelt refusing to kill a bear cub, so inspiring the name 'Teddy's Bear'.

17

18

19

Lavender bags, mothballs and cedar wood shavings help prevent moths from spoiling your ted's fur.

20

21

Bears can be cleaned using a vacuum on a gentle setting, covered with cloth to avoid direct contact with the fur. Wash using soapsuds (not soapy liquid) from a gentle detergent, or mild upholstery fabric cleaner, applied with a soft-bristled brush. Be sure to first test the suds on a concealed spot such as under your bear's arm.

November

22

23

In 1952 Sooty, the gold teddy glove puppet owned by Harry Corbett, first appeared on British T.V.

24

25

26

The large U.S. department store, Macy's, featured an 18-metre/ 59-foot balloon of Smokey Bear in their New York Thanks-giving Day Parade in 1966.

27

28

Saint Andrew's Day

Blueberry Pie

'Berries, black or blue, a bear's favourite food, here's
a tasty recipe to put you in the mood!'

Serves 6

Pastry:
225g/8oz plain flour, sifted
120g/4oz butter or margarine
A little cold milk
Filling:
450g/1lb blueberries, fresh or
    frozen
2 tbsps cornflour
60ml/4 tbsps water
2 tbsps lemon juice
225g/8oz sugar
1 egg, beaten with a pinch of salt

Preheat oven: 220° C/425° F/Gas
Mark 7. **Pastry**: rub the fat into
the flour and stir in enough cold
milk to make a firm dough. Cover
and chill for 30 minutes. Divide
dough in two and roll out half to
fit a 25cm/10-inch pie dish,
pressing well into the sides. Chill.
Filling: mix the cornflour with
the water and lemon juice and

pour over fruit. Add the sugar
and mix gently. Spoon the filling
into the chilled pie shell. Roll out
the rest of the dough and cut into
strips. Make a lattice pattern on
top of the filling and press the

edges to join the pie shell. Use a
fork to crimp edges. Brush with
the beaten egg and bake for about
10 minutes. Reduce the heat to
180° C/350° F/Gas Mark 4 and
bake for a further 40-45 minutes.

December

Christmas has arrived, to end this fine year
Full of warmth and happiness and festive cheer.
Stock up the shelves, pile the honey pots high,
Time to bring friends round as parties draw nigh.
We're so easy to please, we don't ask for much,
Just happy and glad that we've all stayed in touch!

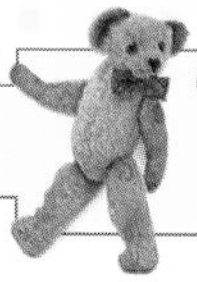

December

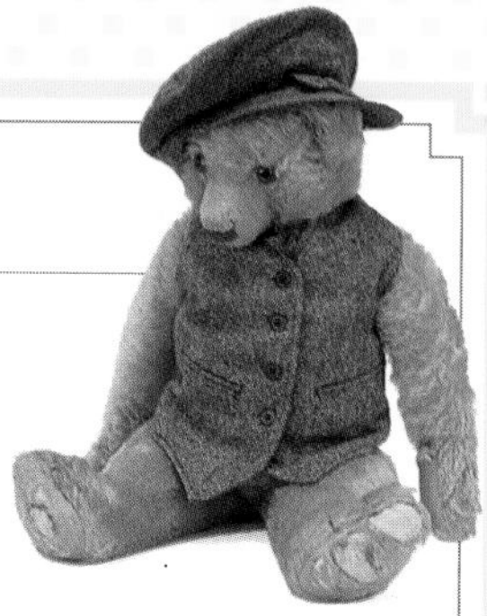

CAPRICORN
22 December - 20 January

1

2

3

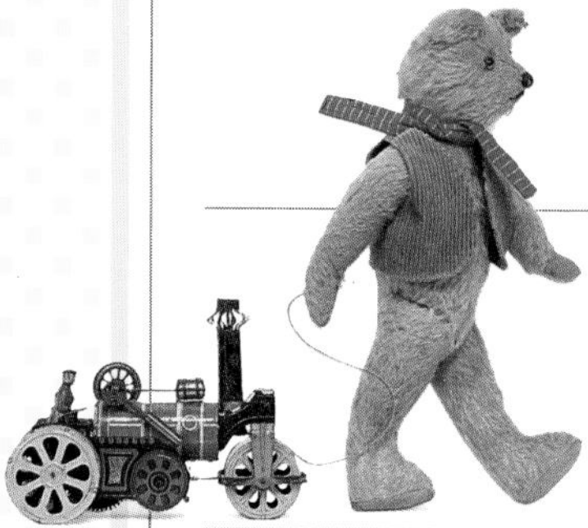

4

5

6

The popular U.S. magazine *Teddy Bear Review* was first published in late 1987.

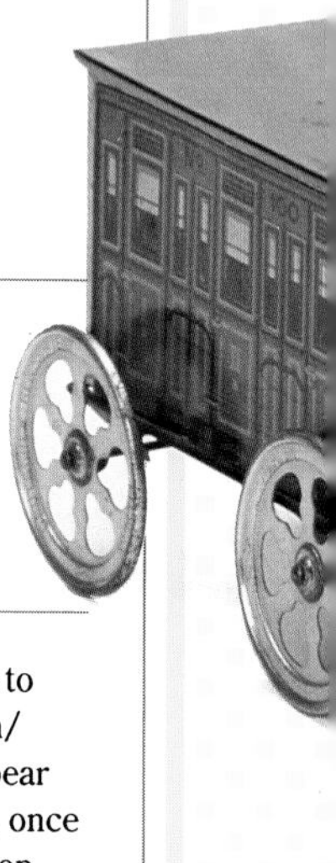

7

Possibly the smallest bears to exist are a tiny teddy 30mm/1.2 inches tall and a silver bear model 7mm/0.3 inches tall, once owned by Colonel Henderson.

Maroon-coloured passports, with space for entering photographs, visas and identifying features, can be bought for your ted from most teddy bear shops. Some custom officials will happily stamp these so that you can keep track of where your bear has visited!

8

9

1988: the 'First Teddy Bear Convention', a three-day event, was held at Orlando, Florida, and featured a two-metre/seven-foot Steiff bear named Hans Willie.

10

11

12

Perhaps the best-known teddy bear story is that of *Goldilocks and the Three Bears*, which was based on a story first printed in the 1830s.

13

14

December

15

16

17

The *Teddy Bear Times* is a popular
teddy publication widely distributed
both in America and in Britain.

18

19

'Y is for Yuletide,
The grown people's name
For the time when my Teddy
From Santa Claus came.'

Anon

20

21

Of all the countries of the world, none has more folk tales about bears than Russia, where for centuries children have been mesmerized by the creature. One of the most popular of the Russian bears, Mishka found his way to Western Europe with the wonderful tale of a toy bear who received the gift of life for Christmas and, after running off to the freedom of the hills, returned to find even greater joy with the poor sick boy who had always loved him.

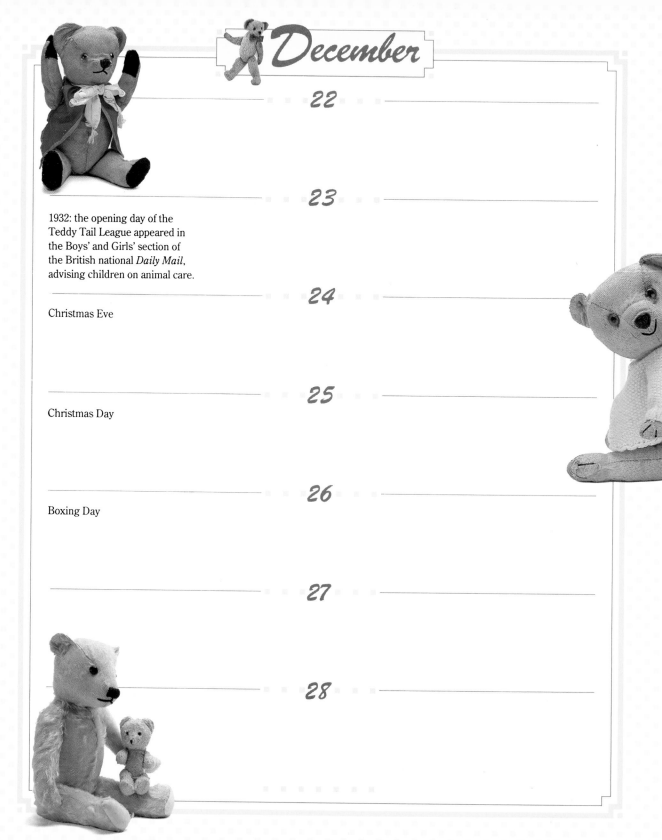

December

22

23

1932: the opening day of the
Teddy Tail League appeared in
the Boys' and Girls' section of
the British national *Daily Mail*,
advising children on animal care.

24

Christmas Eve

25

Christmas Day

26

Boxing Day

27

28

29

30

1965: birth of Rudyard Kipling, author of the popular children's *The Jungle Book*, which features the loveable Baloo Bear, among other characters.

31

New Year's Eve

Honey Shortbread

'We cannot live on honey alone' is an old Japanese proverb, but teds certainly try!'

Shortbread:
340g/12oz plain flour
1 tsp baking powder
1 tsp bicarbonate of soda
280ml/½ pint olive oil
60g/2oz sugar
140ml/¼ pint brandy
60ml/4 tbsps orange juice
1 tbsp grated orange rind
60g/2oz walnuts, chopped
1 tsp ground cinnamon
Syrup:
280ml/½ pint honey
120g/4oz sugar
280ml/½ pint water

Preheat oven: 180°C/350°F/Gas Mark 4. **Shortbread**: sift flour,

baking powder and soda together. Combine oil, sugar, brandy, orange juice and rind. Gradually add the dry ingredients until the mixture comes together. Shape into ovals about 7.5cm/3 inches long and place well apart on several greased baking sheets. Cook for about 20 minutes. Cool.
Syrup: mix the syrup ingredients together and bring to the boil. Boil rapidly for about 5 minutes to thicken. Allow to cool. Dip the cooled shortbread into the syrup and sprinkle with nuts and cinnamon to decorate. Allow to set slightly before serving.

AQUARIUS
21 January - 18 February

Often possessing a deep social conscience, Aquarian bears tend to be tolerant of human behaviour and are quietly affectionate and caring, concentrating more on developing strong friendships than romances. These loyal but complex teds possess an unpredictable and eccentric quality, sometimes compassionate and warm, and at other times cool and detached. Usually very stubborn, and often unconventional and rebellious, Aquarians tend to believe 'I am what I am'!

PISCES
19 February - 19 March

Piscean bears tend to be dreamy and sensitive idealists, with a great imagination and a strong desire for peace. Generous and hard-working, but often unworldly and indecisive, the Piscean teddy is a deeply emotional and intuitive character who loves people and is an incurable romantic. Unassuming and adaptable, these teds make extremely understanding and supportive companions.

ARIES
20 March - 20 April

Arien teds, born under the sign of the ram, are renowned for their constant energy and vitality and the active life-styles they lead, often being the enthusiastic and dynamic initiators of new adventures. These teddies tend to be demonstrative and generous with their hugs and affection and usually possess the ability to make friends easily. But, despite their warmth, take care not to provoke the fiery and volatile Arien teddy temper which is so easily aroused!

TAURUS
21 April - 21 May

Born under the sign of the Bull, it is not surprising that Taurean bears are stubborn and determined characters. Slow to anger and usually possessing unlimited patience, these practical and strong-minded teds make dependable and patient friends. A need for security often causes Taurean teds to be protective, and sometimes very jealous, of their owners and homes. Owners should ensure the stocks of honey are kept high for these affectionate, food-loving bears!

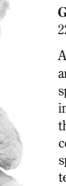

GEMINI
22 May - 21 June

Also known as the sign of the Twins, Gemini bears are known for their versatile, unpredictable and spontaneous natures. Never boring, abounding in energy, and with a pleasure-seeking nature, these teddies make playful and stimulating companions. Known for their talkativeness and speed of thought, and for their more puzzling tendencies, these secretive teds definitely keep their owners on their toes!

CANCER
22 June - 22 July

Cancerian teddies make loyal friends, often demonstrating affection and compassion for others, particularly their owners and more defenceless teds. But their romantic and gentle natures often cause these bears to be oversensitive and vulnerable and even a little gullible. Both home-loving and material-orientated, Cancerians tend to be very domestic and, although fair, extremely careful with their money and belongings – you can guarantee these bears will have a stack of honey stashed away, ready for that rainy day!

Bearoscopes

LEO
23 July - 23 August

Leo bears often display their royal natures with self-confident, sometimes arrogant and proud, demeanours. With a strong flair for drama and arts they tend to be flamboyant, colourful characters, demanding plenty of attention and respect, but always lavishly repaying the affection and love they crave. Generous and big hearted, these teddies are often surprisingly insecure and shy beneath their bold exterior but, owners be warned when taking these bears out, as the Leo ted will always steal the limelight!

VIRGO
24 August - 23 September

Virgo teddies are methodical and highly organized with a tendency to be very neat. Sensitive, well-controlled and independent, they make very agreeable companions and, above all, are extremely reliable. Often possessing a fascination with health and cleanliness, these logical bears dislike living amid clutter and will usually have their owner's life ordered down to the very last detail!

LIBRA
24 September - 23 October

As the sign of the scales suggests, Libran bears are real lovers of harmony, peace and justice, tending to be well-balanced and diplomatic. With senses finely tuned to their owner's mood, and with a strong dislike of argument, the charming Libran makes a perfect companion. The head usually rules the heart of these popular teddies, but they are appreciative of subtle romance. Librans also love their comforts and the finer points of life, so ensure you buy only the best for these refined and elegant teds!

SCORPIO
24 October - 22 November

Scorpio teddies have boundless energy motivated by intense passions, strong beliefs and a fierce pride. Sometimes excessively stubborn, and often enigmatic, Scorpians can be great manipulators of their owners and are usually very determined about what they want. At times cynical, they certainly enjoy undivided attention, so owners beware, these bears are prone to deep jealousy if rival teddies appear on the scene!

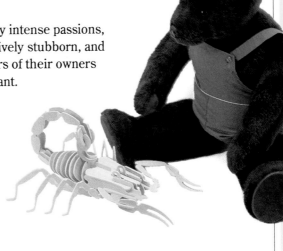

SAGITTARIUS
23 November - 21 December

Adventurous and extroverted, thoughtful and generous, Sagittarian bears are happy-go-lucky, impulsive individuals who are always fun to have around. But their exuberant enjoyment of travel and an active lifestyle often causes these teds to be restless, and frequently a little careless, so owners should be constantly on the look out to rescue their teds from sticky situations!

CAPRICORN
22 December - 20 January

Capricorns tend to be mature bears who frequently possess a solemn and self-sufficient air, but who make loyal and steadfast friends. Often resourceful, these teds like to be in charge of a situation and enjoy security, disliking unexpected change. Quietly determined and usually very disciplined, these protective bears can also be surprisingly ambitious for both themselves and their owners and certainly ensure that things get done!

Credits

The publishers would like to thank the following:

for the loan of their teddy bears:
Elaine Chandler of Peter & Vivien Bradley Antiques, Guildford; Paul Goble
of Bears & Friends, Brighton; Linda Alcock, Mark Alcock, Ruth Arthur,
Janet Berwer, Ruth Bradley, Jill Coote, Angela Flanagan, Brendan Flanagan,
Sarah Kendall, Eileen Lawrence, Betty Little, Sue Pearson, Betty Roy,
Janice Seymour, Rebekka Simons, Colin Speller, Sally Strugnell;

for the use of teddy bears, props and/or locations:
The Cotswold Teddy Bear Museum, Broadway;
Museum of Childhood, Ribchester;
London Toy and Model Museum, London;
Preston Manor, Brighton, courtesy of Brighton Borough Council;

for the loan of various props:
Fiona Eels, Catherine Galvin, Fleur Robertson,
David Searle, Sue Walmsley;

for text contributions:
Bill Harris, Steve Kirkby, Judy Oswald, Paul Richardson,
Andrea Szabados, Lisa Wigley;

for permission to reproduce various extracts:
Methuen Children's Books, for lines from *Winnie-the-Pooh* and *The House
at Pooh Corner* by A.A. Milne;
John Murray (Publishers) Ltd., for lines from *Summoned by Bells* by Sir John Betjeman;
William Collins, an imprint of HarperCollins Publishers Ltd., for lines from
The Adventures of Paddington by Michael Bond.